Magical Mandalas
COLORING BOOK

Alberta Hutchinson

Dover Publications, Inc.
Mineola, New York

Bibliographical Note

Magical Mandalas Coloring Book, first published by Dover Publications, Inc., in 2015, contains all the plates from the following previously published Dover books by Alberta Hutchinson: *Square Mandalas Coloring Book* (2012) and *Magical Mandalas Coloring Book* (2015).

International Standard Book Number
ISBN-13: 978-0-486-80529-0
ISBN-10: 0-486-80529-8

This 2015 edition printed for Barnes & Noble, Inc., by Dover Publications, Inc.

Manufactured in the United States by Courier Corporation